HOW TO READ A COMIC BOOK

Comic books are made up of pictures in boxes, called panels. Look at each of these panels from left to right, and top to bottom.

Read the speech bubbles, caption boxes and any sound effects from left to right, too. Together with the images, these will tell you the story.

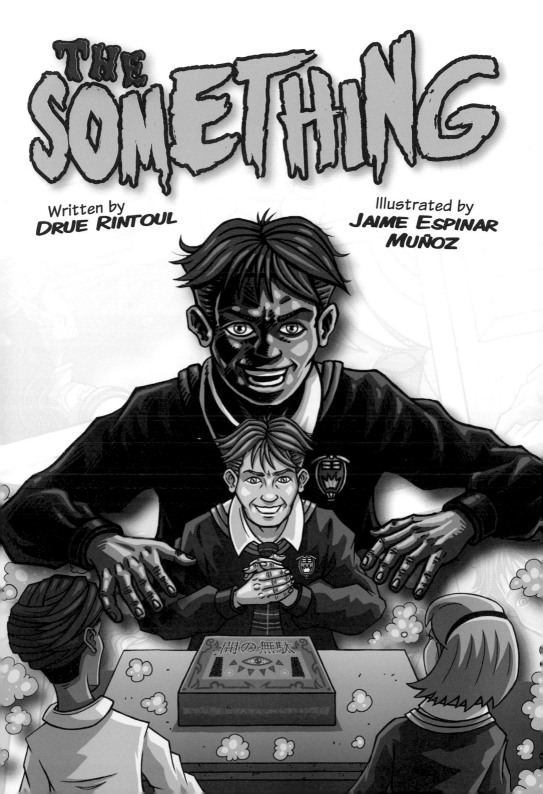

It was a Thursday evening and the Redmont High football team were staying late to practise.

They were the coolest kids in school, and everyone at Redmont loved them.

Well, almost everyone...

Ugh... sports fiends. They think they own the place... always looking down on us.

Johnny...?

Pea-brained sports fiends...

JOHNNY!

Huh?

Are we actually playing today?

Oh, sorry! Hang on...

As you step into the tavern, you see a pale-faced woman at the bar.

You approach her. She slowly raises her eyes to meet yours and you see a look of despair on her face.

13

You open the door a little and peer through the crack. You feel uneasy but must push on.

As the last part of you squeezes through the door...

SLAM!

You try the door.

Locked...

Which way now?

Left...

... or right?

You set off to find the source of the light...

Here goes nothing...

... along corridor after corridor...

... down a long staircase...

... and into the basement...

... where you find a door.

This must be it.

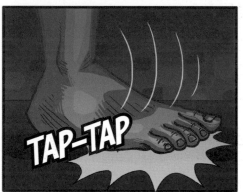

As the words leave your mouth, your torch goes out and you find yourself frozen with fear.

The figure turns to you, and you can see its true form.

THE SOMETHING!

Suddenly, it rushes towards you...

CRASH

THUD

Dead.

Have either of you two got the time?

About 10:30.

How long was I out for?!

I'm not sure. A minute or so?

We were playing for 5 hours? How's that even possible?

Heh, beats me. I guess time just went quickly today.

TAP-TAP

Johnny remembered the words of the barkeep.

...as if time had sped up.

At the front entrance to the school.

Locked. Shoot.

What?! It can't be!

So, we're locked in the school, the power is out and we're using torches?

... just like in the game! This can't be good...

Johnny, I think that football has sent you sideways. You should probably sit down.

It'll be fine. I'll just call my mum for help.

It couldn't have got them, could it? It's not real after all. It's just a game...

TAP-TAP

TAP-TAP

Johnny froze in fear. Tap-tap... tap-tap... like the Something.

Johnny's once football-hating friend was now doing kick-ups.

What do I do?! I need to get out of here, away from these...things—

TAP-TAP

Bad news, I'm afraid.

Huh?

I can't get through. There's just noise and static... must be some kind of problem or something. Listen.

Calling...
Mum

Sure enough, the line was full of static.

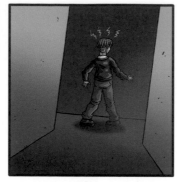

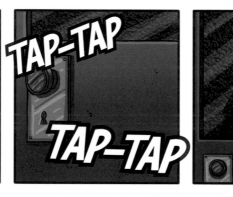

Stay back! You're one of them, aren't you?! You've been changed. I bet you're a sports fiend like them now, too!

It was Mr Leaner, the janitor.

Ha! I was never one for physical activity, my boy - more of a music man myself.

See? I only ever wear band shirts, never sports shirts.

THANKFUL LATE

1985 LD TOUR

But... the game! The Something! My friends - they're... gone!

29

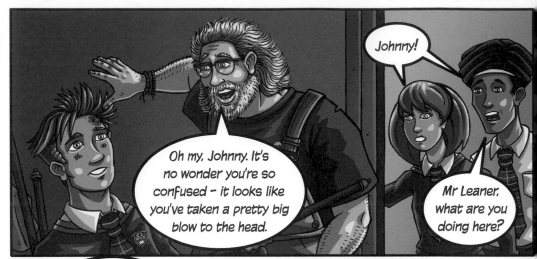

Johnny!

Oh my, Johnny. It's no wonder you're so confused – it looks like you've taken a pretty big blow to the head.

Mr Leaner, what are you doing here?

I came to see what had set the alarm off when I found Johnny hiding in my cupboard.

His head's banged up pretty bad. You two should get him home.

I'm not going anywhere with you! The Something changed you – you're sports fiends now!

I've always been a 'sports fiend'! I just don't mention it around you because you get all weird about sporty people.

Yeah... me too, dude. I've always loved football. Come on, Johnny. Let's get you home.

One week later...

Thanks again for moving Board Game Club to Wednesdays, man. Coach says we have a shot at making the team!

Yeah, thanks Johnny – I always wanted to play with you guys, but football practice always got in the way.

You're welcome... er... I'm sorry, but I didn't catch your name?

Some people call me Hinges, but you can call me Tom.

Tom Hinges... TH on the ball!

Johnny began to rearrange the letters in his head and his worst fear was confirmed.

Tom Hinges...

Something.

©2023 BookLife Publishing Ltd.
King's Lynn, Norfolk PE30 4LS

ISBN 978-1-80155-927-0

The Something
Written by Drue Rintoul
Illustrated by Jaime Espinar Muñoz

ABOUT BOOKLIFE GRAPHIC READERS

BookLife Graphic Readers are designed to encourage reluctant readers to take the next step in their reading adventure. These books are a perfect accompaniment to the BookLife Readers phonics scheme and are designed to be read by children who have a good grasp on reading but are reluctant to pick up a full-prose book. Graphic Readers combine graphic and prose storytelling in a way that aids comprehension and presents a more accessible reading experience for reluctant readers and lovers of comic books.

ABOUT THE AUTHOR

Normally a designer and illustrator by trade, Norfolk-born Drue has been a member of the BookLife Publishing team since its inception, where he has worked on hundreds of books. His passion for illustration began as a child, and he continues to pursue this love both inside and outside of work. Drue resides in King's Lynn with his partner and cat.

ABOUT THE ILLUSTRATOR

Jamie Espinar Muñoz's love for art was passed down to him as part of his family heritage. He is the son, grandson and brother of artists. Jamie studied Fine Arts in college and has extensive experience creating art in a variety of mediums and for different projects, including painting scenery for theatre and television. He has been producing custom illustrations since 2005, working in advertising, magazines, online media and publishing. Now, Jamie is focused on creating illustrations for children's books, comics and even games. He currently resides in Spain with his wife, who works as a graphic designer, his son and their two cats.